Twenty-five Favourite Classics Everybody Loves To Hear

Volume 1
Classical All-Organ Library
Arranged by Kenneth Baker

Amsco Music Publishing
New York/London/Sydney/Cologne

Contents

Foreword *Page 5*

Bach, J S (1685-1750)
Toccata in D Minor *Page 6*

Bach/Gounod C F (1818-1893)
Ave Maria *Page 15*

Beethoven, L V (1770-1827)
Pastoral Symphony (Last Movement) *Page 18*

Borodin, A P (1833-1887)
Polovetzian Dances (Love Theme) *Page 27*

Brahms, J (1833-1897)
Violin Concerto (First Movement) *Page 37*

Chopin, F F (1810-1849)
✳ Nocturne in E Flat *Page 31*

Clarke, J circa (1674-1707)
Trumpet Voluntary *Page 13*

Glinka, M I (1804-1857)
Russlan and Ludmilla Overture *Page 44*

Grieg, E (1843-1907)
Piano Concerto (First Movement) *Page 53*

Handel, G F (1685-1759)
I Know That My Redeemer Liveth *Page 59*
(from "The Messiah")

Khatchaturian, A (Born 1903) ✳
'Spartacus' (Love Theme) *Page 65*

Mendelssohn, F (1809-1847)
Scherzo from "A Midsummer Night's Dream" *Page 73*

Niccolai, O E (1810-1849)
'The Merry Wives of Windsor' Overture *Page 68*

Offenbach, J (1819-1880)
Barcarolle *Page 85*
(from "The Tales of Hoffmann")

Rachmaninoff, S V (1873-1943)
Prelude *Page 89*

Rimsky-Korsakow, N A (1844-1908)
Scheherezade (First Movement) *Page 108*
Scheherezade (Second Movement) *Page 113*

Saint-Saens, C C (1835-1921)
Danse Macabre *Page 95*

Schubert, F P (1797-1828)
Unfinished Symphony *Page 121*

Strauss, J (1825-1899)
Tritsch Tratsch Polka *Page 101*

Tchaikowsky, P I (1840-1893)
March of the Toys *Page 133*
Dance of the Sugar Plum Fairy *Page 139*
Russian Dance *Page 136*
(from "The Nutcracker Suite")

Verdi, G F F (1813-1901)
Celeste Aida *Page 143*

Wagner, R (1813-1883)
Bridal Chorus *Page 130*
(from "Lohengrin")

Directory of Musical Terms, *Page 148*
Basic Chord Chart *Page 153*

Foreword

These two books together contain fifty of the most famous and best loved Classical works ever written.

There are orchestral pieces, songs, piano pieces; extracts from The Ballet, Chamber Music, and Grand Opera.

The pieces have been arranged as simply as possible and are suitable for all organs.

Chord Symbols have been included throughout for those organists unfamiliar with the Bass Clef and at the back of the books there are Basic Chord Charts.

I am sure you will enjoy this great music.

Kenneth Baker

Toccata in D Minor

Bach, J S (1685-1750)

SUGGESTED REGISTRATIONS

General Electronic and Pipe Organs

1	Upper:	Flute 16, 8, 4, 2, String 4, Quint, Nazard
	Lower:	Flute 8, 4, Diapason 8
	Pedal:	16 + 8
	Vibrato:	Off (Leslie: Chorale)
2	Upper:	ADD Trumpet 8
3	Upper:	Flute 16 OFF
4	Upper:	Flute 16 ON
5	Upper:	Trumpet 8, String 4 OFF
6	Upper:	Trumpet 8, String 4 ON

Drawbar Organs

1	Upper:	86 8868 446
	Lower:	(00) 6666 444 (2)
	Pedal:	7- (4)
	Vibrato:	Off (Leslie: Chorale)
2	Upper:	86 8888 654
3	Upper:	00 8888 654
4	Upper:	86 8888 654
5	Upper:	86 8808 004
6	Upper:	86 8888 654

Trumpet Voluntary

Clarke, J circa (1674-1707)

SUGGESTED REGISTRATIONS

General Electronic and Pipe Organs

① Upper: Trumpet 8   *FLUTE 8' 8'OBOE*

Lower: Diapason 8, Flute 8, *HORN 8'*

Pedal: 16+8 *+SUS*

Vibrato: Off   *→ DELAY VIB*

② Upper: ADD Trombone 16

Drawbar Organs

① Upper: 00 8887 652 (0)

Lower: (00) 8764 000 (0)

Pedal: 6 - (4)

Vibrato: Off

② Upper: 76 8887 652 (0)

Ave Maria

Bach/Gounod C F (1818-1893)

SUGGESTED REGISTRATION

General Electronic and Pipe Organs	Drawbar Organs
Upper: Oboe 8, Flute 4	Upper: 00 2678 540
Lower: Flute 8, Diapason 8	Lower: (00) 7632 100 (0)
Pedal: 8	Pedal: 4- (2)
Vibrato: On, medium	Vibrato: On, medium

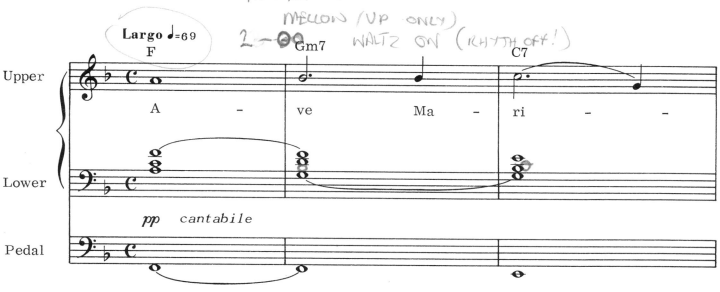

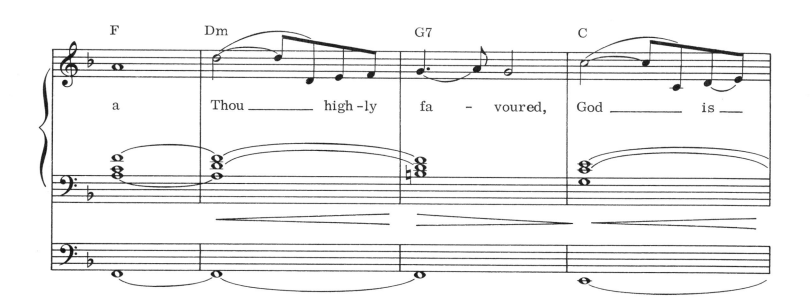

Pastoral Symphony (Last Movement)

Beethoven, L V (1770-1827)

SUGGESTED REGISTRATIONS

General Electronic and Pipe Organs		Drawbar Organs	
① Upper:	Cello 16 (or Flute 16), String 8	① Upper:	50 2345 555
Lower:	Flute 8, Diapason 8	Lower:	(00) 7654 000
Pedal:	16 + 8	Pedal:	5- (3)
Vibrato:	On, full	Vibrato:	On, full
② Upper:	ADD Flute 8, 4	② Upper:	50 7645 555
③ Upper:	String 8 OFF	③ Upper:	50 7605 005
④ Upper:	ADD Oboe 8 (Reed 8)	④ Upper:	50 4685 005

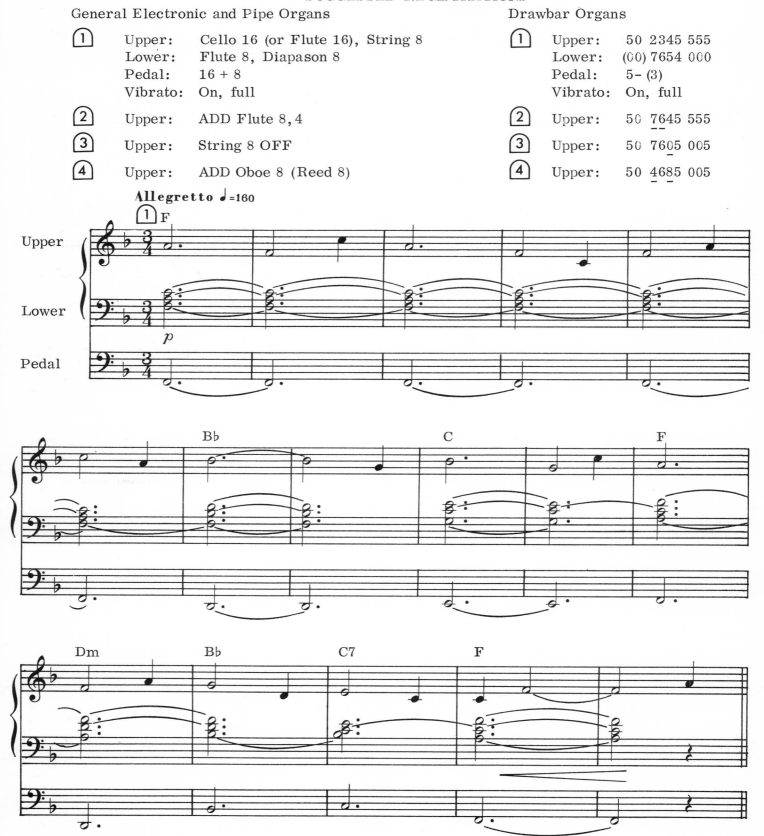

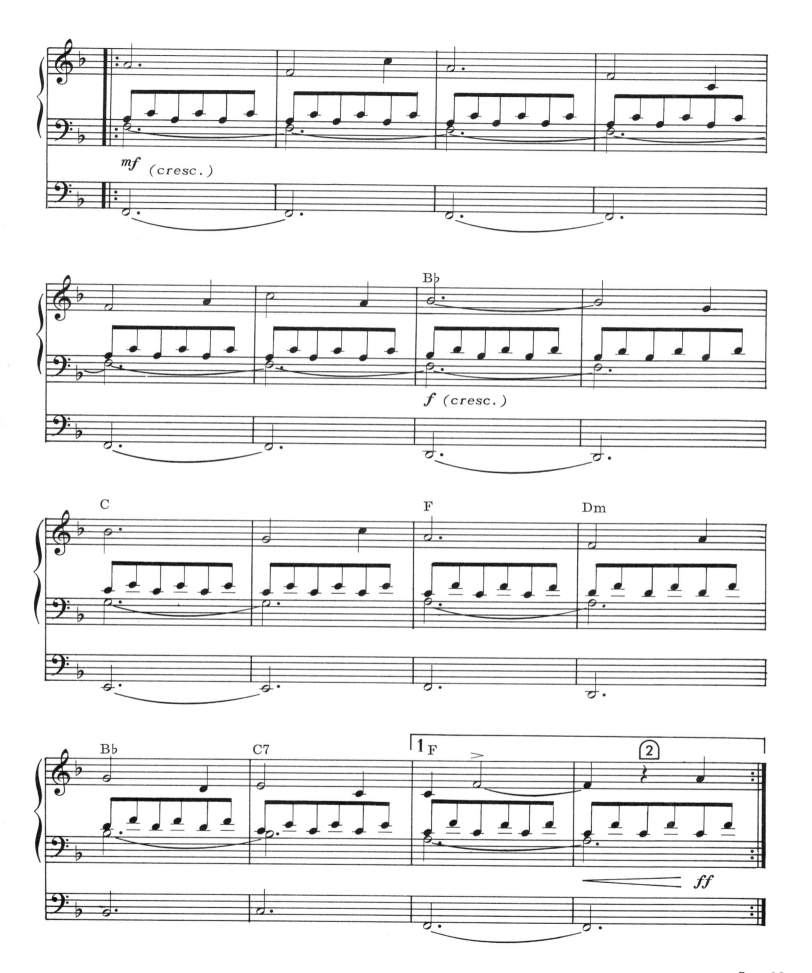

Polovetzian Dances (Love Theme)

Borodin, A P (1833-1887)

SUGGESTED REGISTRATIONS

General Electronic and Pipe Organs

①	Upper:	Oboe 8
	Lower:	Flute 8, ~~Diapason~~ 8
	Pedal:	16 + 8
	Vibrato:	On, ~~medium~~ DELAY VIB ON
②	Upper:	Oboe 8 OFF, Flute 8 ON
③	Upper:	Flute 8 OFF, Oboe 8 ON
④	Upper:	ADD Flute 4

Drawbar Organs

①	Upper:	00 3660 200
	Lower:	(00) 6431 100 (0)
	Pedal:	4- (2)
	Vibrato:	On, medium
②	Upper:	00 6421 000
③	Upper:	00 3660 200
④	Upper:	00 3666 200

Nocturne in E Flat

Chopin, F F (1810-1849)

SUGGESTED REGISTRATIONS

General Electronic and Pipe Organs

① Upper: String 8, Clarinet 8
   Lower: Flute 8, 4
   Pedal: 8 +sus
   Vibrato: On, full

② Upper: ADD Reed 8
③ Upper: Reed 8 OFF
④ Upper: ADD Flute 4, 2
⑤ Upper: Flute 4, 2 OFF

Drawbar Organs

① Upper: 00 7787 753
   Lower: (00) 6522 000 (0)
   Pedal: 5- (2)
   Vibrato: On, full

② Upper: 00 8757 234
③ Upper: 00 7787 753
④ Upper: 00 7787 758
⑤ Upper: 00 7787 753

Violin Concerto (First Movement)

Brahms, J (1833-1897)

SUGGESTED REGISTRATIONS

General Electronic and Pipe Organs

①	Upper:	Cello 16 (or Flute 16), Violin 8 (String 8)
	Lower:	Flute 8, 4, Diapason 8
	Pedal:	16 + 8
	Vibrato:	On, full
②	Upper:	Cello 16 (or Flute 16) OFF
③	Upper:	ADD Flute 8
④	Upper:	Flute 8 OFF
⑤	Upper:	ADD Flute 16, 8

Drawbar Organs

①	Upper:	60 5666 654
	Lower:	(00) 6543 211 (0)
	Pedal:	5-(3)
	Vibrato:	On, full
②	Upper:	00 5666 654
③	Upper:	00 8666 654
④	Upper:	00 5666 654
⑤	Upper:	80 8666 654

Russlan and Ludmilla Overture

§ **Glinka, M I (1804-1857)**

SUGGESTED REGISTRATIONS

General Electronic and Pipe Organs

① Upper: Flute 16, 8, 4, 2
Lower: Flute 8, 4, Diapason 8
Pedal: 16 + 8
Vibrato: On, full

② Upper: ADD: Trumpet 8, Twelfth 2 ⅔

Drawbar Organs

① Upper: 40 8843 210
Lower: (00) 6732 000 (0)
Pedal: 5 - (3)
Vibrato: On, full

② Upper: 43 8865 310

Piano Concerto (First Movement)

Grieg, E (1843-1907)

SUGGESTED REGISTRATIONS

General Electronic and Pipe Organs

1. Upper: Piano Stop (see Organ Manufacturer's Handbook) Or: Flute 16, 8, 4, 2
   Lower: Flute 8, 4
   Pedal: 16 + 8
   Vibrato: Off (with Piano Stop) On, full (with Flutes)

2. Upper: Oboe 8 (Reed 8)
   Lower: Flute 8, 4
   Pedal: 16 + 8
   Vibrato: On, medium

3. Upper: Oboe 8, Flute 8, Clarinet 8
   Lower: Flute 8, 4
   Pedal: 16 + 8
   Vibrato: On, full

Drawbar Organs

1. Upper: 80 8606 004
   Lower: (00) 6534 333(0)
   Pedal: 5 - (3)
   Vibrato: On, full

2. Upper: 00 4675 320
   Lower: (00) 6432 000(0)
   Pedal: 5 - (3)
   Vibrato: On, medium

3. Upper: 01 6475 321
   Lower: (00) 4454 420(0)
   Pedal: 5 - (3)
   Vibrato: On, full

I Know That My Redeemer Liveth (from 'The Messiah')

Handel, G F (1685-1759)

SUGGESTED REGISTRATIONS

General Electronic and Pipe Organs		Drawbar Organs	
(1) Upper: Flute 8 Lower: Diapason 8 Pedal: 8 Vibrato: On, medium		(1) Upper: 00 8400 000 Lower: (00) 4534 110 (0) Pedal: 4- (2) Vibrato: On, medium	
(2) Upper: ADD Flute 4		(2) Upper: 00 8800 000	
(3) Upper: Flute 4 OFF		(3) Upper: 00 8400 000	
(4) Upper: Flute 8 OFF, Oboe 8 ON		(4) Upper: 00 2600 200	
(5) Upper: Oboe 8 OFF, Flute 8 ON		(5) Upper: 00 8400 000	
(6) Upper: ADD Flute 4		(6) Upper: 00 8800 000	
(7) Upper: Flute 4 OFF		(7) Upper: 00 8400 000	

Spartacus (Love Theme)

Khatchaturian, A (Born 1903)

SUGGESTED REGISTRATIONS

General Electronic and Pipe Organs

1.   Upper: String 8, String 4
                  (or Salicet 4)
     Lower: Flute 8, Diapason 8
     Pedal: 16 & 8
     Vibrato: On, full

2.   Upper: ADD Cello 16

Drawbar Organs

1.   Upper: 00 7756 333

     Lower: (00) 7643 100 (0)
     Pedal: 5- (3)
     Vibrato: On, full

2.   Upper: 40 8756 333

This arrangement Copyright 1975 by Dorsey Brothers Music Limited, c/o 19-20 Poland Street, London W1V 3DD

"The Merry Wives of Windsor" Overture

Niccolai, O E (1810-1849)

SUGGESTED REGISTRATIONS

General Electronic and Pipe Organs

① Upper: String 8
Lower: Flute 8, Diapason 8
Pedal: 8
Vibrato: On, full

② Upper: ADD Clarinet 8

③ Upper: ADD Flute 16

Drawbar Organs

① Upper: 00 4566 753
Lower: (00) 7756 310 (0)
Pedal: 4- (2)
Vibrato: On, full

② Upper: 00 7787 753

③ Upper: 80 7787 753

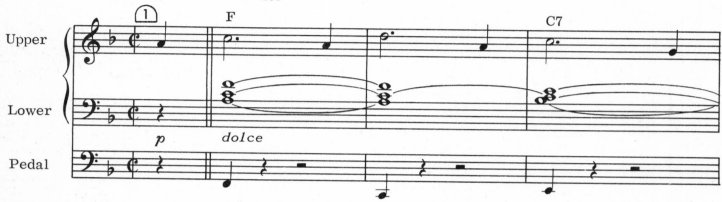

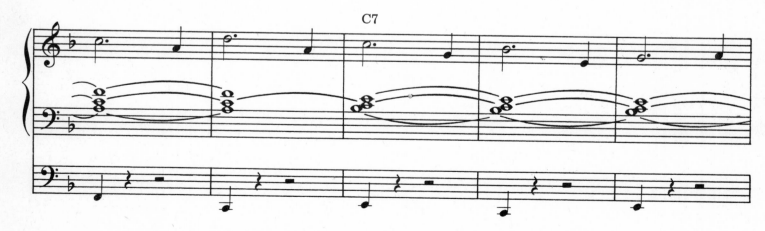

Scherzo from "A Midsummer Night's Dream"

Mendelssohn, F (1809-1847)

SUGGESTED REGISTRATIONS

General Electronic and Pipe Organs

① Upper: Flute 16, 8, 4, 2
    Lower: Flute 8, 4, Diapason 8
    Pedal: 8
    Vibrato: On, full

② Upper: ADD Reed 8 (Oboe 8)

③ Upper: Reed 8 OFF

Drawbar Organs

① Upper: 30 8843 210
    Lower: (00) 6732 000 (0)
    Pedal: 4- (3)
    Vibrato: On, full

② Upper: 30 8866 210

③ Upper: 30 8843 210

Barcarolle (from "The Tales of Hoffmann")

Offenbach, J (1819-1880)

SUGGESTED REGISTRATION

General Electronic and Pipe Organs		Drawbar Organs	
Upper:	Flute 16, 8, 4, 2, Quint, Nazard.	Upper:	80 8805 423
Lower:	Flute 8, 4, Diapason 8	Lower:	(00) 8863 240 (0)
Pedal:	16 + 8	Pedal:	5- (3)
Vibrato:	On, full	Vibrato:	On, full

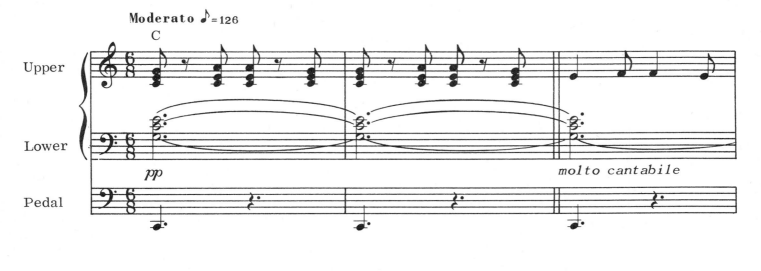

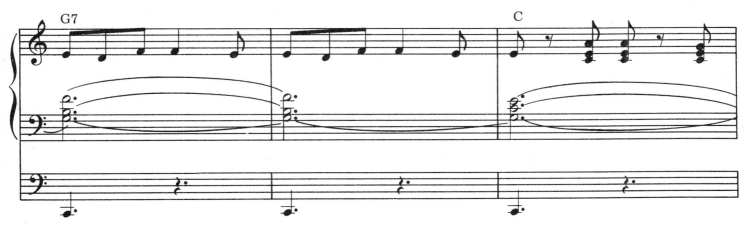

Prelude

Rachmaninoff, S V (1873-1943)

SUGGESTED REGISTRATIONS

General Electronic and Pipe Organs

1. Upper: Flute 16, 8, 4, 2
   Lower: Flute 8, 4, Diapason 8
   Pedal: 16 + 8
   Vibrato: On, full
2. Upper: ADD Horn 8 (or Trumpet 8)
3. Upper: ADD String 8
4. Upper: Horn 8, String 8 OFF

Drawbar Organs

1. Upper: 40 8843 210
   Lower: (00) 6753 211 (0)
   Pedal: 6- (4)
   Vibrato: On, full
2. Upper: 40 8865 210
3. Upper: 42 8885 542
4. Upper: 40 8843 210

Danse Macabre

Saint-Saens, C C (1835-1921)

SUGGESTED REGISTRATIONS

General Electronic and Pipe Organs

1. Upper: String 8
   Lower: Flute 8, 4
   Pedal: 8
   Vibrato: Off
2. Upper: ADD Trombone 16 (or Flute 16)
3. Upper: Trombone 16 (or Flute 16) OFF

Drawbar Organs

1. Upper: 00 4566 788
   Lower: (00) 6732 000 (0)
   Pedal: 4- (2)
   Vibrato: Off
2. Upper: 42 4566 788
3. Upper: 00 4566 788

Tritsch Tratsch Polka

Strauss, J (1825-1899)

SUGGESTED REGISTRATIONS

General Electronic and Pipe Organs

(1) Upper: Flute 16, 8, 4
Lower: Flute 8, 4, Diapason 8
Pedal: 8
Vibrato: On, full

(2) Upper: ADD Flute 2

(3) Upper: ADD Diapason 8 (or Horn 8)

(4) Upper: Diapason 8 (or Horn 8) OFF

(5) Upper: ADD String 4.

(6) Upper: String 4 OFF

Drawbar Organs

(1) Upper: 72 5014 002
Lower: (00) 6443 423 (0)
Pedal: 5- (3)
Vibrato: On, full

(2) Upper: 72 5018 002

(3) Upper: 72 5818 002

(4) Upper: 72 5018 002

(5) Upper: 72 5018 233

(6) Upper: 72 5018 002

TREM ON.

Scheherezade (Movement I)

Rimsky-Korsakow, N A (1844-1908)

SUGGESTED REGISTRATIONS

General Electronic and Pipe Organs

① Upper: Trombone 16, Bassoon 8
Clarinet 8, Oboe 8 (Reed 8)
Lower: Flute 8, 4
Pedal: 16 + 8
Vibrato: On, full

② Upper: Violin 8 (String 8)
Lower: Flute 8, 4
Pedal: 8
Vibrato: On, full

③ Upper: Flute 16, 8, 4, 2
Lower: Flute 8, String 8
Pedal: 16 + 8
Vibrato: On, full

Drawbar Organs

① Upper: 74 6835 000
Lower: (00) 6853 553(0)
Pedal: 6 - (4)
Vibrato: On, full

② Upper: 00 5666 654
Lower: (00) 6533 000
Pedal: 5 - (3)
Vibrato: On, full

③ Upper: 88 8830 300
Lower: (00) 4653 453(0)
Pedal: 5 - (4)
Vibrato: On, full

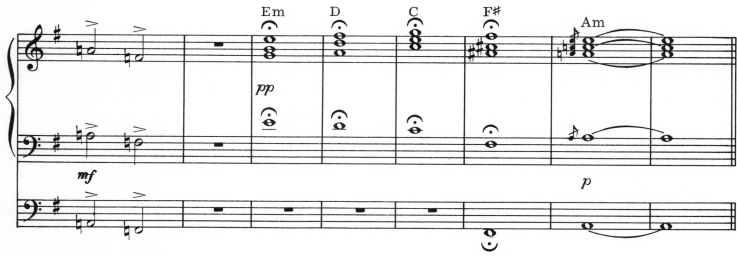

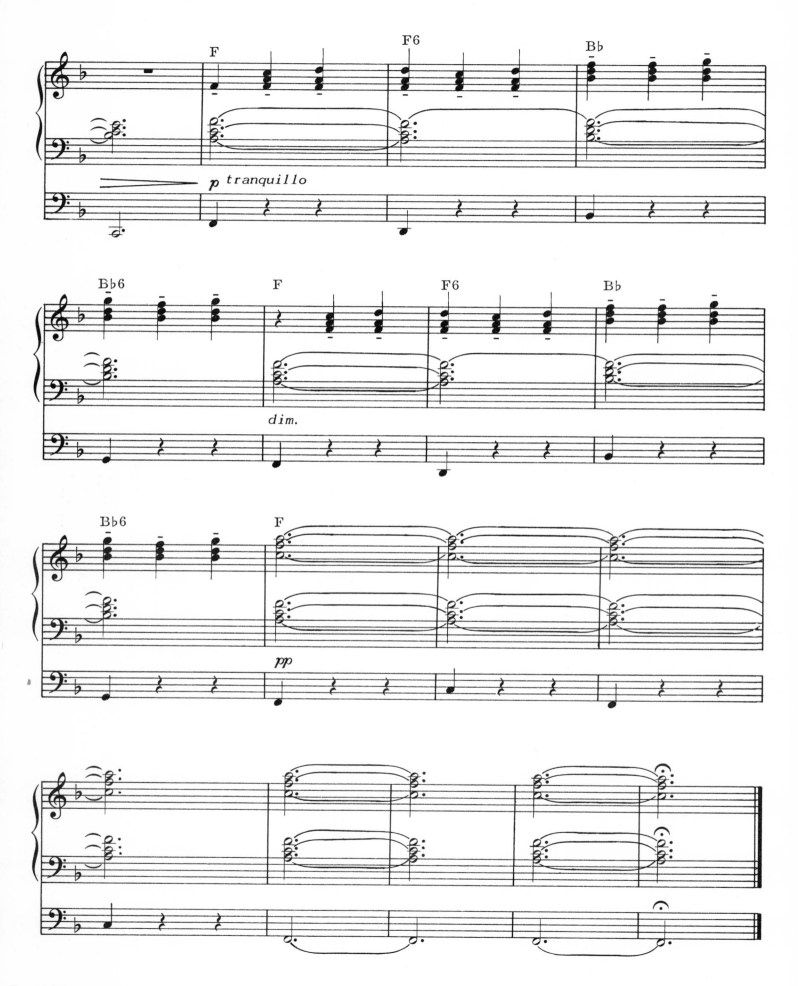

Scheherezade (Movement II)

Rimsky-Korsakow, N A (1844-1908)

SUGGESTED REGISTRATIONS

General Electronic and Pipe Organs

1. Upper: Oboe 8 (Reed 8)
   Lower: Flute 8, 4
   Pedal: 8
   Vibrato: On, small

2. Upper: Violin 8 (String 8)
   Lower: Flute 8, 4
   Pedal: 8
   Vibrato: On, full

3. Upper: Trumpet 8
   Lower: Flute 8, 4
   Pedal: 16 + 8
   Vibrato: Off (Upper Manual)
   On (Lower Manual)

4. Upper: Trumpet 8, Violin 8
   (String 8), Clarinet 8
   Lower: Flute 8, 4
   Pedal: 16 + 8
   Vibrato: On, normal

Drawbar Organs

1. Upper: 00 4675 320
   Lower: (00) 6432 000(0)
   Pedal: 5 – (2)
   Vibrato: On, small

2. Upper: 00 5666 654
   Lower: (00) 6432 000(0)
   Pedal: 5 – (2)
   Vibrato: On, full

3. Upper: 00 8888 888
   Lower: (00) 6660 000(0)
   Pedal: 6 – (4)
   Vibrato: Off (Upper Manual)
   On (Lower Manual)

4. Upper: 00 8888 654
   Lower: (00) 6660 000(0)
   Pedal: 6 – (4)
   Vibrato: On, normal

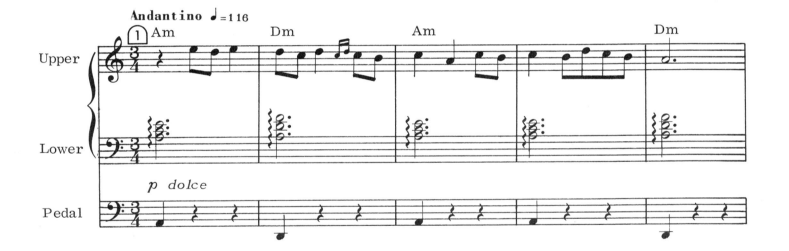

Unfinished Symphony

Schubert, F P (1797-1828)

SUGGESTED REGISTRATIONS

General Electronic and Pipe Organs

①
Upper:	Oboe 8, Flute 8
Lower:	String 8, Horn 8
Pedal:	16+8
Vibrato:	On, medium

②
Upper:	Cello 16, String 8
Lower:	Flute 8, 4, Diapason 8
Vibrato:	On, full

③
Upper:	Flute 8, 4
Pedal:	8

④
Upper:	ADD Flute 2 (or Piccolo 2)

⑤
Upper:	ADD Clarinet 8

⑥
Upper:	Clarinet 8 OFF

Drawbar Organs

①
Upper:	01 6475 321
Lower:	(00) 5565 521 (0)
Pedal:	5- (3)
Vibrato:	On, medium

②
Upper:	50 2345 555
Lower:	(00) 6555 321 (0)
Vibrato:	On, full

③
Upper:	00 7600 000
Pedal:	4- (2)

④
Upper:	00 8706 000

⑤
Upper:	00 8757 344

⑥
Upper:	00 8706 000

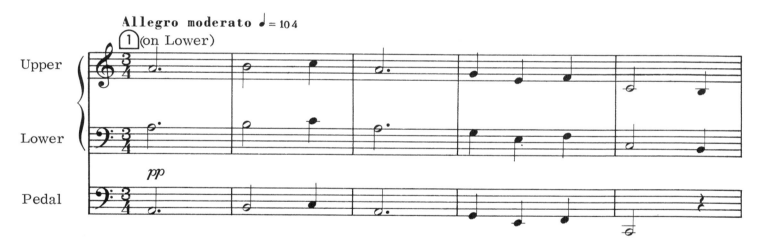

Bridal Chorus (from "Lohengrin")"

Wagner, R (1813-1883)

SUGGESTED REGISTRATIONS

General Electronic and Pipe Organs		Drawbar Organs	
1	Upper: Trumpet 8	1	Upper: 00 7877 420
	Lower: Flute 8, 4, Diapason 8		Lower: (00) 6845 322 (0)
	Pedal: 16 + 8		Pedal: 6- (4)
	Vibrato: Off		Vibrato: Off
2	Upper: Trumpet 8 OFF, Clarinet 8 ON	2	Upper: 00 7272 420
3	Upper: ADD Trumpet 8	3	Upper: 00 7874 420
4	Upper: ADD Flute 16, 8, 4, 2	4	Upper: 70 8874 424

March of the Toys (from "The Nutcracker Suite")

Tchaikowsky, P I (1840-1893)

SUGGESTED REGISTRATION

General Electronic and Pipe Organs		Drawbar Organs	
Upper:	Trombone 16 (or Flute 16), FLUTES 3, 4, OBOE 3' Trumpet 8	Upper:	76 8878 667
Lower:	Flute 8, 4, Diapason 8 HORN 8'	Lower:	(00) 6876 540 (0)
Pedal:	16 + 8 + SUS.	Pedal:	6- (4)
Vibrato:	Off	Vibrato:	Off

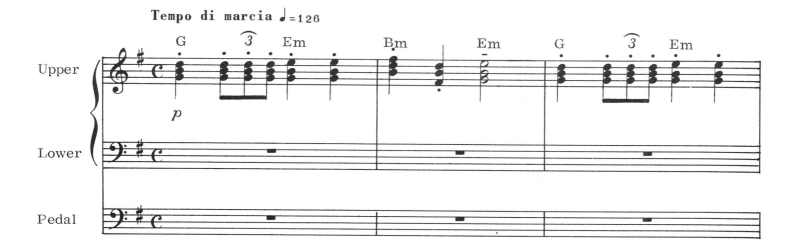

Russian Dance (from "The Nutcracker Suite")

Tchaikowsky, P I (1840-1893)

SUGGESTED REGISTRATION

General Electronic and Pipe Organs

Upper: Flute 16, 8, 4, String 8
Lower: Flute 8, 4, Diapason 8
Pedal: 16 + 8
Vibrato: On, full

Drawbar Organs

Upper: 40 8744 321
Lower: (00) 7654 200 (0)
Pedal: 6- (3)
Vibrato: On, full

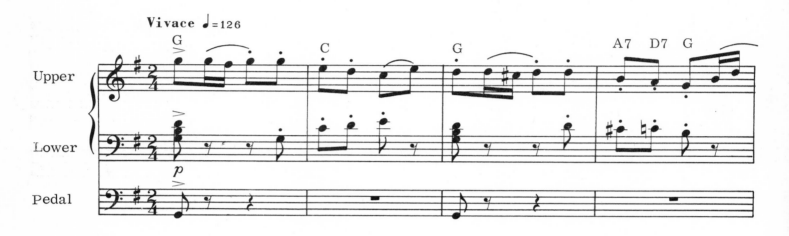

This arrangement Copyright 1975 by Dorsey Brothers Music Limited, c/o 19-20 Poland Street, London W1V 3DD

Dance of the Sugar Plum Fairy (from "The Nutcracker Suite")

Tchaikowsky, P I (1840-1893)

SUGGESTED REGISTRATIONS

General Electronic and Pipe Organs

① Upper: Celeste (or Flute 4, Full Sustain)

   Lower: Flute 8, Horn 8
   Pedal: 8
   Vibrato: Off

② Upper: ADD Flute 16, 8

③ Upper: Flute 16, 8 OFF

Drawbar Organs

① Upper: 00 0803 030
   (with full sustain)
   Lower: (00) 6544 200 (0)
   Pedal: 5- (3)
   Vibrato: Off

② Upper: 40 8803 030

③ Upper: 00 0803 030

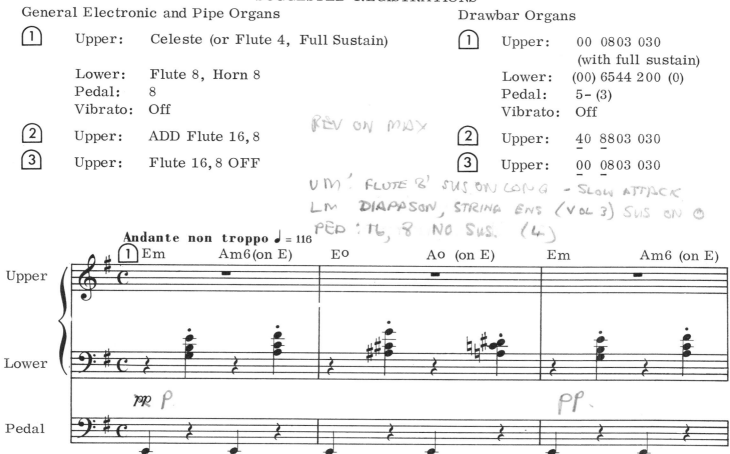

This arrangement Copyright 1975 by Dorsey Brothers Music Limited, c/o 19-20 Poland Street, London W1V 3DD

Celeste Aida

Verdi, G F F (1813-1901)

SUGGESTED REGISTRATIONS

General Electronic and Pipe Organs		Drawbar Organs	
1 Upper: Cello 16		**1** Upper: 40 5545 330	
Lower: Flute 8, 4		Lower: (00) 6343 000 (0)	
Pedal: 16 + 8		Pedal: 4- (2)	
Vibrato: On, full		Vibrato: On, full	
2 Upper: ADD Flute 8, 4		**2** Upper: 40 8645 330	
3 Upper: Flute 8, 4 OFF		**3** Upper: 40 5545 330	
4 Upper: Flute 8, 4 ON		**4** Upper: 40 8645 330	

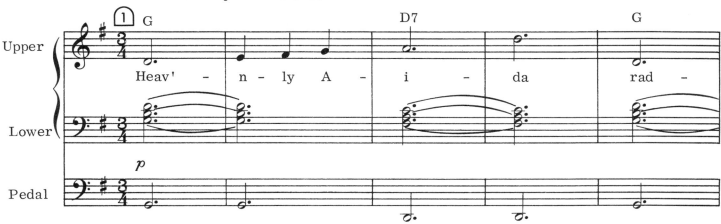

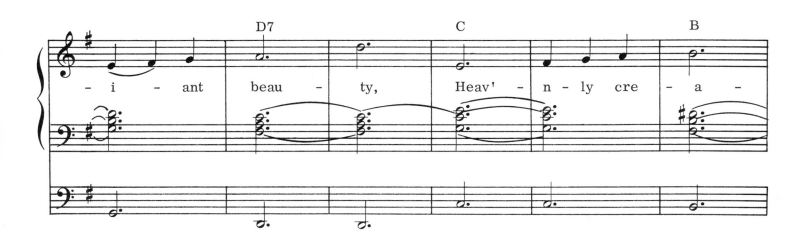

Basic Chord Chart (for left hand)

	C	C♯ (D♭)	D	D♯ (E♭)	E	F
MAJOR (e.g. C)						
MINOR (e.g. Cm)						
DIM. (e.g. C°)						
AUG. (e.g. C+)						
6th (e.g. C6)						
MIN. 6th (e.g. Cm6)						
7th (e.g. C7)						
MIN. 7th (e.g. Cm7)						

For Cmaj7 and Cm(maj7) play C and Cm respectively (similarly in all keys)

For Csus4 and C7sus4 play C and C7 respectively (similarly in all keys)

For Csus2 and Cmsus2 play C and Cm respectively (similarly in all keys)

Basic Chord Chart (for left hand)

For C7+ play C+ (similarly in all keys)

For C7−5 play C7 (similarly in all keys)

For C9, C11, C13 (or variations thereof, e.g. −9, −13) play C7 (similarly in all keys)

Dictionary of Musical Terms

A – in, at, etc. (e.g. A Tempo, in time)

ACCELERANDO (ACCEL.) – getting gradually faster

ADAGIO – Slow

AD LIBITUM (AD LIB.) – At Pleasure, i.e. the tempo and expression are left to the judgement of the performer

AGITATO – In an agitated, restless style

AL – to the (e.g. D.S. AL FINE, from the Sign (𝄋) to the end).

ALLARGANDO (ALLARG.) – broadening: probably slowing down and getting louder

ALLEGRETTO – moderately fast. Somewhat slower than Allegro

ALLEGRO – Quick, lively. Often used in conjunction with other terms, e.g. Allegro Moderato, moderately quick

ANDANTE – literally: "walking". Indicates a somewhat slow tempo. Often used in conjunction with other terms, e.g. Andante Con Moto, slowly, but with some movement, Andante Con Espressione, slowly, with expression

ANDANTINO – true meaning: slightly slower than Andante; usual meaning (as here) slightly *faster* than Andante

ANIMANDO – with animation

A PIACERE – at the pleasure of the performer

APPASSIONATO – passionately

ASSAI – very. e.g. Rit. Assai, slowing down a great deal

A TEMPO – in time. i.e. the original speed is to be resumed

BEN – well. e.g. Ben Cantando, in a strong singing style

CALMO – calm, tranquil

CANTABILE – in a singing style

CANTANDO – in a singing style

CAPRICCIOSO – in a capricious, fanciful style

COME – as. e.g. Come Prima, as at first

CON – with. Used in conjunction with other terms, e.g. Con Espressione, with expression; Con Grazia, with Grace

CRESCENDO (CRESC.) OR – ⦦ gradually getting louder. Often used in conjunction with other terms, e.g. Crescendo poco a poco, getting louder little by little

DAL – e.g. Dal Segno (D.S.), from the Sign (𝄋)

DELICATISSIMO – most delicately

DI – of. e.g. Tempo Di Valse, Tempo of the Waltz

DIMINUENDO (DIM.) OR ⦧ getting softer

DOLCE – sweet, soft

DOLCE E ESPRESSIVO – sweetly and expressively

DOLCEMENTE – sweetly

E – and. Used in conjunction with other terms, e.g. Dolce e Espressivo, sweetly and expressively

ESPRESSIONE – expression. e.g. Con Espressione, with expression

ESPRESSIVO (ESPRESS.) – expressively

FINE – the end. e.g. D.S. al FINE: from the Sign (𝄋) to the end).

FORTE – (*f*) loud. (*ff*, very loud; *fff*, as loudly as possible)

FORTE PIANO (*fp*) – Loud–soft. i.e. starting loudly and immediately reducing the tone

FORZA – force. e.g. Con Forza, with force

FORZANDO – (*fz*), forcing the tone. Probably a note or chord is to be heavily accented

FRISKA – Quick and fiery

GRAZIA – grace. e.g. Con Grazia, in a graceful, elegant style

GRAZIOSO – gracefully

LARGAMENTE – Broadly (at this point the piece is to be slower and louder)

LARGHETTO – at a slow tempo, but not so slow as Largo

LARGO – large, broad. The term usually indicates an extremely slow and stately movement

LASSAN – Slow and melancholy

LEGATO – (⌢ or ⌣), smooth, joined. The notes are to be played so that there is
          no break between them

LEGGIERO – light, nimble

LENTE – slow. e.g. Tempo Di Valse Lente, slow Waltz tempo

LENTO – slow

LENTO A CAPRICCIOSO – slowly and in a capricious, fanciful style

LISTESSO – the same. e.g. Listesso Tempo, the same time. An indication that the rate
          of pulsation is to remain the same

MAESTOSO – majestically, with dignity

MANCANDO – decreasing in tone, dying away

MARCATO – marked, accented (Marcato Assai, very accented)

MARCIA – a March. A piece of music suitable for accompanying walking

MAZURKA – A national Polish dance in triple time and having a certain accentuation
          on the weaker beats of the bar

MENO – less. e.g. Meno Forte (Meno *f*), less loud; Meno Mosso, less moved: not so fast

MESTO – sad

MEZZO – medium. e.g. Mezzo Forte (*mf*), moderately loud; Mezzo Piano (*mp*), moderately soft

MODERATO – moderate. An indication of the speed of a movement

MODERATO CON MOTO– moderate with motion i.e. rather faster than Moderato

MOLTO – much, very. e.g. Molto Diminuendo (Molto Dim.), getting very much quieter;
          Molto Rallentando (Molto Rall.) getting very much slower

MORENDO – dying away, decreasing in tone

MOTO – motion, movement. e.g. Con Moto, with animated movement

NON – not. e.g. Non Troppo, not too much

OSSIA – optional. e.g. 8va Ossia, the notes may be played an octave higher if the performer so wishes

PASSIONATO – passionately

PASSIONE – passion. e.g. Con Passione, with deep intensity of feeling

PASTORALE – in a pastoral, or rural style

PERDENDO – dying away

PESANTE – heavy, firm

PIANO (*p*) – Soft. Pianissimo (*pp*), very soft. Molto Pianissimo (*ppp*), as softly as possible.

PIANISSIMO SUBITO (*pp* **Subito**) – Suddenly very soft.

PIÙ – more. Used in conjunction with other terms, e.g. Più. Forte (Più *f*), more loudly; Più Allegro, more quickly

POCHISSIMO PIÙ MOSSO – the tiniest bit faster

POCO – a little. Used in conjunction with other terms, e.g. Poco Crescendo, getting a little louder; Poco Mosso, a little bit faster; Poco Più *f*, a little louder; Poco A Poco, little by little; Poco A Poco Accelerando, getting faster little by little

PRESTISSIMO – extremely fast

PRESTO – fast. A degree of speed faster than Allegro

PRIMA – first

QUASI – almost. e.g. Quasi Allegretto, almost Allegretto: moderately fast

RALLENTANDO (**RALL.**) – gradually slowing down

RECITATIVO (**RECIT.**) – recitative. A style of vocal music something between speaking and singing

RINFORZANDO (*rf*) – reinforced. i.e. an increased loudness for a note or chord. An accent

RITENUTO (**RIT.**) – held back; going at a slower rate of speed

SCHERZANDO – in a playful manner

SEMPLICITÀ – in a simple, unaffected style

SEMPRE – always. e.g. Sempre Forte (Sempre *f*), always loud; Sempre Staccato (Sempre Stacc.), the notes being always cut short; Sempre Più *p*, getting softer all the time

SFORZANDO (*sf*) – the note, or chord so marked is to be emphasized

SFORZATO PIANO (*sfp*) – indicates an emphasis, followed by an immediate softness

SIMILE (**SIM.**) – in the same manner, i.e. continue the staccato style, or whatever it is you have been doing, in the same way

SMORZANDO – dying away

SOTTO – under. e.g. Sotto Voce, in an undertone

STACCATO (♩ or ♪) – detached, separated. The notes so marked are to be disconnected from one another

STRETTO – getting gradually faster

STRINGENDO – getting gradually faster. Also used in conjuction with other terms, e.g. Stringendo E Crescendo, getting gradually faster and louder; Stringendo Poco a Poco, getting faster little by little

SUBITO – quick, sudden. e.g. *pp* Subito, suddenly very soft

TEMPO – the rate of speed, or movement. Thus: Tempo Di Marcia, the speed of a March; Tempo Primo, the speed as at first

TENUTO (TEN.) – held back

TRANQUILLO – in a quiet, tranquil style

TREMOLO – the rapid alternation of notes (as marked) on a keyboard

TRILL (𝆖𝅦) – the regular and rapid alternation of a note and the note next above (either a tone, or a semitone distant)

TRIO – a subordinate division of the piece, usually in a contrasted key and style

TROPPO – too much. e.g. Allegro Non Troppo, fast, but not too fast

UN – a. e.g. Un Poco Più Allegro, a little faster

VALSE – Waltz. A dance form in triple rhythm

VIBRATO (VIB.) – a tremulous effect; an oscillation of the note(s)

VIVACE – lively, animated. Used in conjunction with other terms, e.g. Allegro Vivace, lively and even faster than Allegro

VIVO – lively, briskly

VOCE – voice. e.g. Sotto Voce, under the voice; in an undertone

MISCELLANEOUS SIGNS

—	Accent
>	Accent (Heavier)
<	Crescendo (getting louder)
>	Diminuendo (getting softer)
♪ ♩	Staccato (cut short)
♩ ♩ ♩	Detached, but not as short as Staccato
⌒	Fermata (Pause)

//   Break (in sound and time)

C   Common Time: $\frac{4}{4}$

¢   Cut Common Time: $\frac{2}{2}$ A feeling of 2 in a bar rather than 4

Tie. A rhythmic device; an extension of the note(s) in time. Only applies when the notes connected are the same.

Legato. The notes are to be played in a smooth, joined–up manner. (The notes here will *not* be the same).

ves – sel

Phrase mark for Lyric. The syllable "ves" is to be sung on two different notes.

Double bar line. A new section is about to begin.

Repeat marks. The section between the two marks is to be repeated. If there is no earlier Repeat Mark to go back to, go back to the beginning of the piece.

1

The bars (Measures) enclosed by the bracket here must be played on the 1st time through only. The player will then go back and make his repeat.

2

The bars (Measures) enclosed by the bracket here will be played on the 2nd time through only. The player will then play on. (Unless he has reached the end of the piece).

8va---------- The notes concerned are to be played an octave higher than written.

%   Sign. A point in the piece to go back to in order to play that particular section again. The instruction to go back will read: D.S. (Dal Segno), meaning: go back to Sign.

Acciaccatura. A short "grace" note to be played as quickly as possible before the main note.

Several such "grace" notes, to be played as quickly as possible before the main note.

Arpeggio. The notes of the chord are to be played in rapid succession upwards.

Printed in Great Britain by
St Edmundsbury Press, Bury St Edmunds, Suffolk